Audition Songs
Female Singers 11

Murder On The Dancefloor...

plus eight more dance anthems
ideal for auditions

THIS PUBLICATION IS NOT AUTHORISED FOR SALE IN
THE UNITED STATES OF AMERICA AND/OR CANADA.

Wise Publications
London/New York/Paris/Sydney/Copenhagen/Berlin/Madrid/Tokyo

Murder On The Dancefloor

Words & Music by Gregg Alexander & Sophie Ellis-Bextor

© COPYRIGHT 2001 KEEPIN IT REAL HOW BOUT YOU MUSIC/
WARNER/CHAPPELL MUSIC LIMITED (82.5%)/RONDOR MUSIC (LONDON) LIMITED (17.5%).
ALL RIGHTS RESERVED. INTERNATIONAL COPYRIGHT SECURED.

know, I know, I know, I know, I know, I know,_ I know   a- bout_ your

(Verse 2 see block lyric)

kind._   And

so, and so,_ and so,   and so, and so,   and so,_ and so   I'll have_ to

play._

Hey, hey, hey.___ It's

mur - der on the dance - floor___ but you'd bet - ter not steal the moves___

___ D. J. Gon - na burn this god - damn house right down.
2° turn this house a - round some - how.

2. Oh I

1.

2.

Mur - der on the dance - floor,___ (on the dance - floor) but you'd bet - ter not kill the groove.___

Hey, hey,___ hey.___ It's mur - der on the dance - floor___ (On the dance - floor.) but you'd bet - ter not steal the moves.___ D. J. Gon - na burn this god - damn house right down.___

Guitar

burn this god - damn house right down. It's mur - der on the dance - floor _____

Verse 2:
Oh, I know, I know, I know, I know, I know, I know, I know
There may be others
And so, and so, and so, and so, and so, and so, and so
You'll just have to pray
If you think you're getting away
I will prove you wrong
I'll take you all the way
Stay another song, I'll blow you all away.

Hey, it's murder on the dancefloor *etc.*

Castles In The Sky

Words & Music by Erik Vanspauwen,
Christophe Chantzis & Martine Theeuwen

© COPYRIGHT 2001 A&S PRODUCTIONS/BE SONGS/SHERLOCK HOLMES MUSIC LIMITED.
ALL RIGHTS RESERVED. INTERNATIONAL COPYRIGHT SECURED.

Oh, tell me why___

do we___ build cas - tles in___ the sky?___ Oh, tell___ me why_

are the cas- tles way_ up high._

_ Please tell_ me why_ do we_ build cas-

- tles in_ the sky._ Oh, tell_ me why_

are the cas- tles way_ up high._

Hungry

Words & Music by Darren Beale, Mark Morrison & Sian Evans

© COPYRIGHT 2001 TAIRONA SONGS LIMITED.
ALL RIGHTS RESERVED. INTERNATIONAL COPYRIGHT SECURED.

1. You're like a child with old eyes,
(Verse 2 see block lyric)

cy - ni - cal and sen - si - ble, al - ways full of sur - prise.

You're like a sight for sore eyes, ly - ri - cal and__ gen - tle__ and bor - der - lin - ing sen - ti - men - tal.__ You're like a dream re - al - ised, so

wet your ap-pe - tite._____   Are you hun - gry?_____

Verse 2:
Now give me this mountainside
Cool water, to lie beside
Give me these two strong eyes
To see the difference between truth and lies
Oh, give me this feeling
When you kiss me baby, every day and every night
That's all I need, yes
Everything else gonna be alright.

Are you hungry *etc.*

Heaven

Words & Music by Bryan Adams & Jim Vallance

© COPYRIGHT 1984 IRVING MUSIC INCORPORATED/ADAMS COMMUNICATIONS INCORPORATED/
ALMO MUSIC CORPORATION/TESTATYME MUSIC, USA. RONDOR MUSIC (LONDON) LIMITED.
ALL RIGHTS RESERVED. INTERNATIONAL COPYRIGHT SECURED.

We're in hea - ven.

- lieve,   we're in hea - ven.

And lov - ing is all___ that I   need,   and I've found   it there_ in your

heart.   It is - n't too hard___ to see____   we're in hea-

- ven.   We're in hea - ven.

I Turn To You

Words & Music by Melanie Chisholm, Rick Nowels & Billy Steinberg

© COPYRIGHT 1999 EMI MUSIC PUBLISHING (WP) LIMITED (33.33%)/JERK AWAKE/
EMI APRIL MUSIC INCORPORATED/FUTURE FURNISHING MUSIC/EMI MUSIC PUBLISHING LIMITED (66.67%).
ALL RIGHTS RESERVED. INTERNATIONAL COPYRIGHT SECURED.

would I do if you'd nev - er helped me through?

I hope some - day, if you lost

your way, you could turn to me, like I turn

to you.

Set You Free

Words & Music by Michael Lewis, Dale Longworth & Kevin O'Toole

© COPYRIGHT 1994 ALL BOYS MUSIC LIMITED.
ALL RIGHTS RESERVED. INTERNATIONAL COPYRIGHT SECURED.

Verse 2:
When we touch each other
In a state of ecstacy
Want this night to last forever
Only love can set you free.

Silence

Words & Music by Bill Leeb, Rhys Fulber & Sarah McLachlan

© COPYRIGHT 1997 TYDE MUSIC/SONY/ATV MUSIC PUBLISHING (UK) LIMITED (50%)/
ESOTERIA PUBLISHING/CHRYSALIS MUSIC LIMITED (10.93%)/NETTWERK SONGS PUBLISHING (UK) LIMITED (39.07%).
ALL RIGHTS RESERVED. INTERNATIONAL COPYRIGHT SECURED.

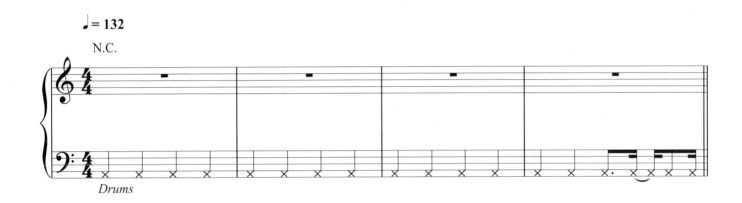

Give me peace.

Hea - ven holds a sense of won - der. And I want - ed to be - lieve that I get caught up when the rage in me sub - sides.

43

Verse 2:
I can't help this longing
Comfort me.
I can't hold it all in
If you won't let me.

Heaven holds a sense of wonder *etc..*

Touch Me

Words & Music by Cassandra Fox, Rui Da Silva & Gary Kemp

© COPYRIGHT 2000 EMI MUSIC PUBLISHING LIMITED (36.5%)/NOTTING HILL MUSIC (UK) LIMITED (33.5%)/
REFORMATION PUBLISHING COMPANY LIMITED (30%).
ALL RIGHTS RESERVED. INTERNATIONAL COPYRIGHT SECURED.

I'm al - ways think - ing____ of____ you ba - by.

Yeah.____

Touch me in the

feel - ing_____ I'll feel it___ with you._____

We___ can on - ly___ un - der - stand what___ we___ are shown.___

How___ was I sup - posed___ to know our___ love___ would

grow.___ Move a lit - tle clos - er,_____ things sure___

Whoa.___ We__ can on - ly__ un-
- der - stand what we___ are shown.
How__ was I sup - posed__ to know our__ love___ would grow?___
You touch my mind__ in spe - cial pla - ces.___

Who Do You Love Now?

Words & Music by Victoria Horn & Jon Riva

© COPYRIGHT 2001 VICTORIA HORN PUBLISHING LIMITED/CHRYSALIS MUSIC LIMITED (50%)/
MONZA MUSIC/UNIVERSAL/MCA MUSIC LIMITED (50%).
ALL RIGHTS RESERVED. INTERNATIONAL COPYRIGHT SECURED.

Verse 2:
A moment of coldness cuts through me
I've tried to remember why I don't leave
And you're the cause of my confusion
Closing down the way I feel
How come I don't see so clearly
So clearly
Fighting to breathe

And it's hard to break a habit *etc.*

Exclusive Distributors:
Music Sales Limited
8/9 Frith Street,
London W1D 3JB, England.
Music Sales Pty Limited
120 Rothschild Avenue,
Rosebery, NSW 2018,
Australia.

Order No. AM959156
ISBN 0-7119-7415-2
This book © Copyright 2003 by Wise Publications

Unauthorised reproduction of any part of this publication by any
means including photocopying is an infringement of copyright.

Music arranged by Derek Jones.
Music processed by Paul Ewers Music Design.

CD recorded, mixed and mastered by Jonas Persson.
Backing tracks arranged by Sensible Footware Productions.
Lead and backing vocals by Elly Barnes.

Cover photograph (Sophie Ellis-Bextor) courtesy of REX.

Printed in the United Kingdom by
Printwise (Haverhill) Limited, Haverhill, Suffolk.

Your Guarantee of Quality
As publishers, we strive to produce every book
to the highest commercial standards.
The music has been freshly engraved and the book has been
carefully designed to minimise awkward page turns and
to make playing from it a real pleasure.
Particular care has been given to specifying acid-free,
neutral-sized paper made from pulps which have not been
elemental chlorine bleached. This pulp is from farmed sustainable
forests and was produced with special regard for the environment.
Throughout, the printing and binding have been planned to ensure a
sturdy, attractive publication which should give years of enjoyment.
If your copy fails to meet our high standards, please inform us and
we will gladly replace it.

www.musicsales.com